Published in the United States by Zerflin, LLC, Baltimore, MD.
Version: The Uniting Center 365 Days of Intentional Living Book 6x8 8
Modified: April 12, 2018 4:10 PM

Compiled and edited by Celeste Viciere
Words by Celeste Viciere
Design & Illustration by Benjamin Jancewicz of Zerflin
Printed in the United States of America

Zerflin.com
books@zerflin.com
931.305.0883

CELESTE VICIERE

TheUnitingCenter.com
info@TheUnitingCenter.com
931.305.0883

365 Days

of INTENTIONAL LIVING

CELESTE VICIERE

Licensed Mental Health Clinician

Intro

One of the most common mistakes we make in our society is failing to self-reflect. If you live in America, you know that we are taught to be successful by getting married, having a car, a house, two kids and a dog. We are not taught that true happiness starts on the inside. America does not teach us to reflect on our life. We are constantly on the go and we do not take time for ourselves. We do not like to look at the hard parts of our life. Why is that? Are they not a part of who we are? We are inauthentic when we try to suppress the negative things or the hard emotions. We lose ourselves.

My name is Celeste Viciere and I am a Licensed Mental Health Clinician. I have a private practice in Boston, MA. I have been in the mental health field for over 15 years. Those years have taught me a lot about people, about what helps them lead more focused, calm inner lives.

Do you want to find yourself, learn what works for you and what doesn't? The purpose of this journal is to have you take intentional time out your day to evaluate different aspects of your life. This journal will allow you to look at all areas of your life and reflect on it.

Please understand that the journaling process can bring up hard emotions and past trauma. If you find yourself struggling and overwhelmed, please seek support from a professional to assist you with this process.

What is self-reflection?

Self-reflection means taking an honest look at yourself, not only the good attributes but also the parts of you that you may feel ashamed of or think is complex. We tend to avoid reflecting on ourselves because of shame.

We struggle with being authentic because it can feel complicated and overwhelming. Self-reflection is hard because thinking about your own negative attributes can feel shameful. If you want to feel comfortable with yourself, it's important to take time out your day to reflect on your complete self.

Why is journaling important?

Journaling is one of the most effective tools I like to use for treatment. We are constantly dealing with everyday life. We are working, going to school, being a mom or dad, being a friend, etc., and we miss out on the moments that can affect us. If you can work on self, you will learn how to have power over your emotions and be able to make clear conscious decisions around situations that affect your life.

What are some common issues with which the guided journal will help?

If you're able to truly delve into this journal, it will cause you to start thinking about different areas in your life. It will force you to bring your unconscious to your conscious. We struggle with dealing with any kind of emotional pain. We are okay with dealing with happy times while struggling with dealing with depression or anxiety. We tend to self-medicate by overworking, eating, partying and shopping. This method of getting through life is not sustainable.

You will feel like you are surviving and not really living your life.
This journal will guide you through a diverse range of topics in your life, including relationships, work environment, school, family and your personal self. As you pause, and self-reflect, you will learn how to understand the things that trigger you.

When you are able to understand your triggers, you can make positive changes in your life. Learning your trigger and comprehending your emotions will allow you to understand yourself and understand how your past can affect your present, as well as help you gain control over your emotions.

How does the journal work?

1. Try and complete each day around the same time. The point is to be intentional in doing this. Of course, when you are starting a routine, things may happen, or you may forget to write one day. That's ok. If you miss a day or two, you can start again on the next day. Set an alarm clock, put it in your calendar. Tell yourself that this is important and make the time for it. You must be intentional.

2. Try and spend a minimum of 15 minutes a day reflecting and writing. If possible, make sure you do not have any distractions. This may mean that you may have to wake up before everyone, do it before bed or during your lunch break. There is no right or wrong time to complete this. There is no right or wrong amount of words. Write what you feel. You can also use the space to draw out your emotions. You must do what works for you.

3. Each day there will be a question or a statement. You can reflect on or respond to the statement or question for the day.

   a. If you are journaling at night, I want you to use this journal to reflect on your day and also think about how you have to prepare for the next day.

   b. If you journal first thing in the morning, think about the events from the day before and contemplate how you are going to prepare for your day.

   c. Did any strong emotions come up for you? Each day, look at the feeling chart on page VI and identify how you are currently feeling. Identify why you think you are feeling the way you are feeling.

4. I understand that there are times when the question or statement for the day may not apply to you. If it doesn't, skip the statement or question, but continue to write about your current feelings and/or anything else you feel may have affected you, positively or negatively. Make sure you are using the chart on page VI to identify your emotion. Try and be more thorough than just, "happy" or "sad".

5. You will notice similar statements and common themes throughout the journal. The goal behind this is to assist you with shifting your thought process and becoming more intentional. The more you hear it, the more it begins to make sense. You will begin to have a deeper understanding.

6. Half way through the journal, you will be asked the same question or statement from the beginning. The purpose is to see how your thoughts have changed through the journaling process. Because you may not be working with a therapist, I wanted to give you a way of identifying the changes being made. If you can work with a therapist, this is a perfect tool that you can use to process your emotions with them.

7. When you notice things that help you cope with negative feelings, write them on page VII & VIII. The goal is to have a list of tools you can use for overcoming negative emotions. I have an example on some positive healthy coping skills you can use on page IX.

Feeling Chart

Use this emotion chart daily to identify how you are feeling.

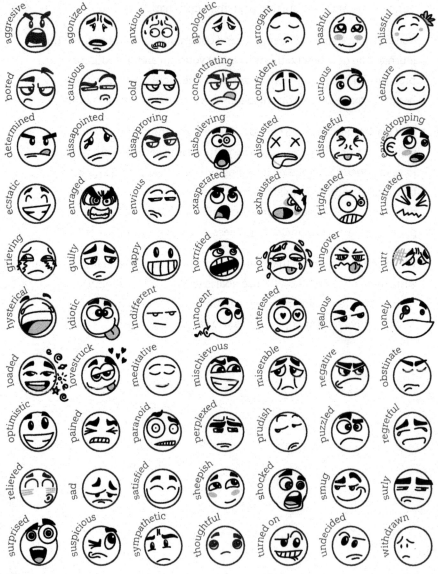

Positive Coping Strategies

Use this space to write down positive coping strategies you used.

Positive Coping Strategies

Use this space to write down positive coping strategies you used.

_____

_____

_____

_____

_____

_____

_____

_____

_____

_____

_____

_____

_____

_____

_____

_____

_____

_____

_____

_____

_____

_____

_____

_____

Examples of coping strategies you can use when you are having negative feelings:

1. Go for a walk
2. Take long deep breaths for 2 minutes
3. Have a hot mug of tea
4. Take a long shower
5. Meditate
6. Listen to music
7. Write poetry
8. Draw
9. See a movie
10. Sing
11. Do a word search or cross word puzzle
12. Allow yourself to cry
13. Clean
14. Learn how to cook
15. Try some aromatherapy
16. Pray
17. Do something creative (painting, sewing, rearrange room)
18. Color with crayons
19. Talk with someone (supportive)
20. If you are spiritual or religious, read the teachings of the religion you subscribe to.
21. Stretch
22. Do yoga
23. Perform a random act of kindness

Examples of coping strategies
you can use when you are
having negative feelings

Day 1
05 / 16 / 2020

Look at the feelings chart to identify how you are feeling
today. Did you know that stigma continues to stop us
from checking in about our mental health? Would you wait to
bandage your bleeding finger? Why do you wait to check in with yourself?
How are you really doing? It's important to be honest with yourself.

Feelings: Dissatisfied. Surly. Frustrated. But also, okay.
Today has been one of those days where it is so
unmistakenly clear that I'm not in control and
that reminder threw me a little. Maybe a lot. The
timing of everything felt off and just did not go
as planned.

Day 2
<u>07</u> /<u>28</u> /<u>20</u>

Look at the feelings chart to identify how you are
feeling today. You must make yourself a priority.
You make that happen by deciding to put YOU first.
Are you putting yourself first?

Enraged. Exhausted. Frustrated. Sad. Sympathetic.
A few words to sum up my feelings over the last
two days. Oh, and hurt. It hurts a lot to
hear and see my little girl ~~seem~~ hurt. She is
hurting herself. She doesn't love herself and I
can't fix it. I have to make sure everything I
say and do is grounded in love. This should help
her understand that she is loved, I hope.

Where are the tears for these cries?

Day 3

___ / ___ / ___

Look at the feelings chart to identify how you are
feeling today. Your actions come from how you
feel, and feelings come from your thoughts.
If you want to change your behaviors, it's important to understand your thoughts.

_____

_____

_____

_____

_____

_____

_____

_____

_____

_____

_____

_____

_____

_____

_____

_____

_____

Day 4
__/__/__

Look at the feelings chart to identify how you are feeling
today. It's okay to say, "I'm not okay." If you want to heal,
its important you start being honest with yourself.
You are human life is a journey.

_____
_____
_____
_____
_____
_____
_____
_____
_____
_____
_____
_____
_____

Day 5

___ / ___ / ___

Look at the feelings chart to identify how you are feeling today.
Angry, frustrated, sad, confused are all normal emotions to have
during hard times. How you handle these emotions is so important.
Do you feel you have control over your emotions?

_____

_____

_____

_____

_____

_____

_____

_____

_____

_____

_____

_____

_____

_____

Day 6
__ / __ / __

Look at the feelings chart to identify how you are feeling
today. Stay mindful on the impact of negative moments
in your life. Sometimes negative moments can impact us in
a negative way. Make sure you have HEALTHY outlets to deal with it.
What healthy outlets do you have?

_____

_____

_____

_____

_____

_____

_____

_____

_____

_____

_____

_____

_____

Day 7

___ / ___ / ___

Look at the feelings chart to identify how you are feeling today.
Sometimes we procrastinate and say, "maybe tomorrow".
We wait to make amends with people; we wait
to start our goals; we wait to really live our lives.
It's important to understand that tomorrow may never come.
Knowing this fact should be motivation to start really living in the NOW.

_____

_____

_____

_____

_____

_____

_____

_____

_____

_____

_____

_____

_____

_____

_____

Day 8

__ / __ / __

Look at the feelings chart to identify how you are
feeling today. Sometimes we are where we are
in life because we do not have an open mind.
We are not open to new opportunities, ways of dealing with emotions or
even listening to advice. When your mind is closed, nothing can leave or go
in. Life is too short to keep doing the same thing getting the same result.

_____

_____

_____

_____

_____

_____

_____

_____

_____

_____

_____

_____

_____

_____

Day 9

___ / ___ / ___

Look at the feelings chart to identify how you are feeling today.
Even though the journey of self-awareness
and loving yourself can be lonely, doing this will
allow you mental stability and emotional freedom.

_____

_____

_____

_____

_____

_____

_____

_____

_____

_____

_____

_____

_____

_____

_____

_____

Day 10
__ / __ / __

Look at the feelings chart to identify how you are
feeling today. Life is a journey full of ups and downs.
We mastered dealing with good times, but we ignore the hard times.
It's hard to live a balanced life when you are ignoring parts of yourself.

_____

_____

_____

_____

_____

_____

_____

_____

_____

_____

_____

_____

_____

Day 11
___ / ___ / ___

Look at the feelings chart to identify how you are feeling today.
Stop asking yourself, "why do people hurt me?" Reframe
the question to, "Why am I allowing people to hurt me?"
When you reframe the question, it helps you feel empowered
and gives you control to make healthy choices.

_____
_____
_____
_____
_____
_____
_____
_____
_____
_____
_____
_____
_____
_____
_____
_____
_____

Day 12

__ / __ / __

Look at the feelings chart to identify how you are feeling
today. Are you waiting for validation to make your next move?
To people out there with no support, understand you can do this.
You have more power than you think, you have to start having faith to believe that.

_____

_____

_____

_____

_____

_____

_____

_____

_____

_____

_____

_____

_____

Day 13
___ / ___ / ___

Look at the feelings chart to identify how you are feeling today.
The best things in life are the moments.
Moments are important decisions and events in your life.
It's time we create beautiful moments that will last a life time.
Are you creating moments?

_____

_____

_____

_____

_____

_____

_____

_____

_____

_____

_____

_____

_____

_____

_____

_____

Day 14
__ / __ / __

Look at the feelings chart to identify how you are feeling today.

Write down some positive changes you can make in your life.

Think of some things you can change today.

_____

_____

_____

_____

_____

_____

_____

_____

_____

_____

_____

_____

Day 15
___/___/___

Look at the feelings chart to identify how you
are feeling today. Change starts with you.
Are you intentionally making positive changes?
Did you implement any changes you wrote down on Day 14?

Day 16
__ / __ / __

Look at the feelings chart to identify how you are feeling today.
Are you creating a life that feels good on the inside
and not one that just looks good on the outside?

_____

_____

_____

_____

_____

_____

_____

_____

_____

_____

_____

_____

_____

_____

Day 17
___ / ___ / ___

Look at the feelings chart to identify how you are feeling today.
Learn how to reframe how you speak about yourself.
Speaking positive over your life is so necessary.
Sometimes we have internal thoughts we are not aware of.
Listen to how you speak about yourself.
Are you being kind to yourself?

_____

_____

_____

_____

_____

_____

_____

_____

_____

_____

_____

_____

_____

_____

_____

Day 18
___ / ___ / ___

Look at the feelings chart to identify how you are feeling
today. Stigma continues to stop people from asking for help.
Would you be ashamed if you cut your finger and it was bleeding?
If you feel you need mental health support, it is important you ask.
Life is too short to continue suffering in silence.

_____

_____

_____

_____

_____

_____

_____

_____

_____

_____

_____

_____

_____

_____

Day 19

__ / __ / __

Look at the feelings chart to identify how you are feeling today.
Often, people tell themselves that when they get a job or more
money they will be happy. For example, some people are waiting for a
promotion at their job. People will say, "Once I become a manager, I will be happy."
We plan for happiness as a future event. How would you describe happiness?

_____

_____

_____

_____

_____

_____

_____

_____

_____

_____

_____

_____

_____

_____

_____

_____

Day 20

__ / __ / __

Look at the feelings chart to identify how you are feeling
today. Many people think they are not happy when they are
not in a relationship. As humans we yearn for someone to love us.
Do you love yourself? You can't depend or look for love solely in other people.
Loving yourself is so important.

Day 21
__ / __ / __

Look at the feelings chart to identify how you are feeling today.
I once heard someone say, "normal is just a dial on
the washing machine." It's important you stop looking at
yourself negatively because you are different from everyone else.
Being different is okay. You are unique and wonderfully made.
Don't forget that.

_____
_____
_____
_____
_____
_____
_____
_____
_____
_____
_____
_____
_____
_____
_____
_____

Day 22
__ / __ / __

Look at the feelings chart to identify how you are feeling today.

Did you know that you are AMAZING?

Do you feel amazing?

Speaking positively about yourself is very important.

Try saying it to yourself now. "I am Amazing."

_____

_____

_____

_____

_____

_____

_____

_____

_____

_____

_____

_____

_____

Look at the feelings chart to identify how you are feeling today.

Did you know there are 86,200 seconds in a day?

Are you making each one count?

_____

_____

_____

_____

_____

_____

_____

_____

_____

_____

_____

_____

_____

_____

_____

_____

Day 24
__/__/__

Look at the feelings chart to identify how you are feeling today.
If you focus on the good things that are happening
in your life, it can change the way you view your life.
What do you find yourself focusing on?

_____

_____

_____

_____

_____

_____

_____

_____

_____

_____

_____

_____

_____

_____

_____

Day 25
___ / ___ / ___

Look at the feelings chart to identify how you are feeling today.
People will treat you how you allow them to treat you.
Are the people in your life kind and supportive to you?

_____
_____
_____
_____
_____
_____
_____
_____
_____
_____
_____
_____
_____
_____

Day 26
___ / ___ / ___

Look at the feelings chart to identify how you are feeling today.
Get rid of the negative people in your life. We
continue to allow them back in our lives. It's time to
learn how to stop the negative cycle so that you can grow.
Always check the people that are in your circle.

_____

_____

_____

_____

_____

_____

_____

_____

_____

_____

_____

_____

_____

Day 27

___/___/___

Look at the feelings chart to identify how you are feeling today.
Are you waiting for validation? Do you wait for
someone to breathe? We breathe alone and if you are
someone who does not have people validating you, keep going.
Stop waiting for someone to say keep going or good job.
Learn how to motivate yourself.

Day 28

___ / ___ / ___

Look at the feelings chart to identify how you are feeling today.
Are you collecting moments or things? Which do you cherish the
most? It's time we create beautiful moments that will last a lifetime.

_____
_____
_____
_____
_____
_____
_____
_____
_____
_____
_____
_____
_____
_____

Day 29
___ / ___ / ___

Look at the feelings chart to identify how you are feeling today.
Are you struggling with trying to make
positive changes in your life? What can you start
doing today to make a positive impact on your life?

_____
_____
_____
_____
_____
_____
_____
_____
_____
_____
_____
_____
_____
_____
_____
_____
_____
_____
_____

Day 30
__ / __ / __

Look at the feelings chart to identify how you are feeling today.
Do you believe in yourself?

_____
_____
_____
_____
_____
_____
_____
_____
_____
_____
_____
_____
_____
_____
_____

Day 31
___ / ___ / ___

Look at the feelings chart to identify how you are feeling today.
Did you know that there is room in life for everyone to win?
Everything is not a competition.
Make sure you focus on yourself and your goals.
We can all bloom together.

_____

_____

_____

_____

_____

_____

_____

_____

_____

_____

_____

_____

_____

_____

_____

_____

Day 32

__ / __ / __

Look at the feelings chart to identify how you are feeling today.
What do you say about yourself? If you find yourself speaking
negative, learn how to reframe how you speak about yourself.
Speaking positive over your life is so necessary.

How are you feeling today?

Day 33

___ / ___ / ___

Look at the feelings chart to identify how you are feeling today.

Do you find yourself focused on the future?

Forget about the future because it's not here.

Stop wasting time worrying; it can continue to cause anxiety in your life.

Leave the future for the future.

_____

_____

_____

_____

_____

_____

_____

_____

_____

_____

_____

_____

_____

_____

_____

_____

_____

Day 34

___ / ___ / ___

Look at the feelings chart to identify how you are feeling today.
Knowing your triggers is an important part of dealing with life.
Do you know the things in your life that hinder
you from moving forward with your goals?
If you say no, start being mindful throughout the day of
how people, things and situations affect you.

_____

_____

_____

_____

_____

_____

_____

_____

_____

_____

_____

_____

_____

Day 35

___ / ___ / ___

Look at the feelings chart to identify how you are feeling today. Life can feel hard at times. The only thing we can do is learn how to truly live and be prepared to deal with the curve balls that are being thrown at us. How do you deal with life?

_____

_____

_____

_____

_____

_____

_____

_____

_____

_____

_____

_____

_____

_____

_____

Day 36
___ / ___ / ___

Look at the feelings chart to identify how you are feeling today.

You have more power than you realize.

You just have to have the faith to believe that.

Do you believe in yourself?

_____

_____

_____

_____

_____

_____

_____

_____

_____

_____

_____

_____

_____

_____

_____

Day 37

___ / ___ / ___

Look at the feelings chart to identify how you are feeling today.
You are okay. Things will get better. You may not believe that
right now but it's important to speak positive over your life.

Day 38
___ / ___ / ___

Look at the feelings chart to identify how you are feeling today.

"I can do this."

Yes, you can absolutely do this.

Never let anyone tell you otherwise.

_____

_____

_____

_____

_____

_____

_____

_____

_____

_____

_____

_____

_____

_____

How are you feeling today?

Look at the feelings chart to identify how you are feeling today.
Running away from your problems will not solve anything.
The only way to deal with internal pain is to deal with it.
Healing starts from the inside.

_____
_____
_____
_____
_____
_____
_____
_____
_____
_____
_____
_____
_____
_____
_____
_____

Day 40
__ / __ / __

Look at the feelings chart to identify how you are feeling today.
Be conscious of what is happening to you mentally.
When you are conscious of it, it's easier to cope
with the uncomfortable feelings you may have.

How are you feeling today?

Day 41
__ / __ / __

Look at the feelings chart to identify how you are feeling today.
It's okay to have emotions and feelings because you are human.
It's important you learn how to deal
with those emotions in a healthy way.
How are you dealing with your emotions?

_____

_____

_____

_____

_____

_____

_____

_____

_____

_____

_____

_____

_____

_____

_____

_____

_____

_____

Day 42

__ / __ / __

Look at the feelings chart to identify how you are feeling today.

Did you know you can end up being a

prisoner when you do not forgive?

You become locked inside the anger or hatred.

Do you find yourself holding anger and hate in your heart for someone?

If you answer yes, how is that helping you?

_____

_____

_____

_____

_____

_____

_____

_____

_____

_____

_____

_____

_____

_____

How are you feeling today?

Day 43
___/___/___

Look at the feelings chart to identify how you are feeling today.
Tell yourself that life is worth living.
Continue to say it and you will believe it.
There is something powerful about having a positive
narrative about your life and destiny.

_____

_____

_____

_____

_____

_____

_____

_____

_____

_____

_____

_____

_____

_____

Day 44
___/___/___

Look at the feelings chart to identify how you are feeling today.

Do you feel like you are searching for happiness?

Have you thought about what happiness means to you?

How do you expect you find it?

_____

_____

_____

_____

_____

_____

_____

_____

_____

_____

_____

_____

_____

_____

_____

Day 45
___ / ___ / ___

Look at the feelings chart to identify how you are feeling today.
Look in the mirror and say, "I love you."
Work on being in love with you.

_____

_____

_____

_____

_____

_____

_____

_____

_____

_____

_____

_____

_____

_____

_____

Day 46
__ / __ / __

Look at the feelings chart to identify how you are feeling today.
When you are sad and alone, your mind can lead
you to believe that your current feelings are permanent.
It is important to understand that feelings are temporary.

_____

_____

_____

_____

_____

_____

_____

_____

_____

_____

_____

_____

_____

Day 47

___ / ___ / ___

Look at the feelings chart to identify how you are feeling today.
People continue to search for balance in life and come up empty.
The problem is that you have to CREATE
a balance life to make it happen.

Day 48
__ / __ / __

Look at the feelings chart to identify how you are feeling today.
Mourn the loss of the life you wanted.
Even if you are not where you want to be, accept
where you are and work on a plan to change.

_____

_____

_____

_____

_____

_____

_____

_____

_____

_____

_____

_____

_____

Day 49

___ / ___ / ___

Look at the feelings chart to identify how you are feeling today.
Do you find yourself rushing through life?
What are you rushing for?

_____

_____

_____

_____

_____

_____

_____

_____

_____

_____

_____

_____

_____

_____

_____

_____

Day 50
__ / __ / __

Look at the feelings chart to identify how you are feeling today.

Do you feel like you are being yourself?

If not, why are you living a filtered life?

Why not just be you?

_____

_____

_____

_____

_____

_____

_____

_____

_____

_____

_____

_____

_____

How are you feeling today?

Day 51

___ / ___ / ___

Look at the feelings chart to identify how you are feeling today.

Self-care is important.

Are you taking care of everyone else?

Life is to short not to take care of yourself.

_____

_____

_____

_____

_____

_____

_____

_____

_____

_____

_____

_____

_____

_____

_____

Day 52

___ / ___ / ___

Look at the feelings chart to identify how you are feeling today.
When you dwell on the past and worry
about the future, you miss out on NOW.
What motto do you live by?

_____

_____

_____

_____

_____

_____

_____

_____

_____

_____

_____

_____

_____

_____

_____

Look at the feelings chart to identify how you are feeling today.

Being intentional is important.

We are intentional about getting dressed and brushing our teeth.

Are you intentional on taking care of your mental health?

_____

_____

_____

_____

_____

_____

_____

_____

_____

_____

_____

_____

_____

_____

_____

_____

Day 54

__ / __ / __

Look at the feelings chart to identify how you are feeling today.
Check your circle. Are your relationships reciprocal?
Do you find yourself always giving of
yourself and not getting anything in return?

_____

_____

_____

_____

_____

_____

_____

_____

_____

_____

_____

_____

_____

_____

Look at the feelings chart to identify how you are feeling today.
We spend too much time on social media and on our phones.
If you feel disconnected from your kids, partner and
yourself, you can try taking a break from social media.
This is so necessary.

Day 56

__ / __ / __

Look at the feelings chart to identify how you are feeling today.
Do you have goals you want to accomplish? Consistency and
commitment is important. Work on it even when you don't feel like it.

_____
_____
_____
_____
_____
_____
_____
_____
_____
_____
_____
_____
_____
_____

Day 57
___ / ___ / ___

Look at the feelings chart to identify how you are feeling today.
'I will do what's best for me." Say that to yourself.

_____

_____

_____

_____

_____

_____

_____

_____

_____

_____

_____

_____

_____

_____

_____

Day 58

___/___/___

Look at the feelings chart to identify how you are feeling today.

It's important to live in the present moment

because you can never get it back.

Do you feel like you are living in the present moment?

_____

_____

_____

_____

_____

_____

_____

_____

_____

_____

_____

_____

_____

Look at the feelings chart to identify how you are feeling today.
People may not understand you and that's okay.
It's important that you are not allowing
other people to get inside your head.
They may never understand you.

_____
_____
_____
_____
_____
_____
_____
_____
_____
_____
_____
_____
_____
_____
_____

Day 60

___ / ___ / ___

Look at the feelings chart to identify how you are feeling today.

It is important that we have a positive narrative about ourselves.

Thinking positive feels better than thinking negative.

Try saying 3 positive things about yourself each day.

_____

_____

_____

_____

_____

_____

_____

_____

_____

_____

_____

_____

_____

_____

Day 61
___ / ___ / ___

Look at the feelings chart to identify how you are feeling today.
It is important you recognize the areas
of your life you can improve on.
What areas of your life can you start working on.

_____

_____

_____

_____

_____

_____

_____

_____

_____

_____

_____

_____

_____

_____

_____

_____

Day 62
__ / __ / __

Look at the feelings chart to identify how you are feeling today.
Did you know that everyone does things at their own pace?
Just because it may have taken you longer to
complete something does not mean you failed.
Remember that.

_____

_____

_____

_____

_____

_____

_____

_____

_____

_____

_____

_____

_____

Day 63
__ / __ / __

Look at the feelings chart to identify how you are feeling today.
Do you want to stop the negative cycles in your life?
It's important we recognize what is causing it.
We have to learn how to heal from our past.

_____
_____
_____
_____
_____
_____
_____
_____
_____
_____
_____
_____
_____
_____
_____
_____
_____

Day 64

___ / ___ / ___

Look at the feelings chart to identify how you are feeling today.
Speaking positive and writing down how you want to
change is a great start. The next step to change is action.
Do you feel like you are actively trying to live an intentional life?

_____

_____

_____

_____

_____

_____

_____

_____

_____

_____

_____

_____

Day 65

___ / ___ / ___

Look at the feelings chart to identify how you are feeling today.
Sometimes we allow what other people
do to have a negative effect on us.
Why do you allow people to control what takes place with your emotions?

_____
_____
_____
_____
_____
_____
_____
_____
_____
_____
_____
_____
_____
_____
_____

Day 66
___/___/___

Look at the feelings chart to identify how you are feeling today.

We make time for things we care about.

How much do you care about yourself?

Are you making time to take care of you?

_____
_____
_____
_____
_____
_____
_____
_____
_____
_____
_____
_____
_____
_____
_____

Look at the feelings chart to identify how you are feeling today.

We say to ourselves, "Tomorrow, I'll do it or "one day I'll do it."

Why not make a plan to start today?

Time waits for no one.

_____

_____

_____

_____

_____

_____

_____

_____

_____

_____

_____

_____

_____

_____

_____

Day 68
___ / ___ / ___

Look at the feelings chart to identify how you are feeling today.

You may not be where you want to be in life; that's okay.

What tends to stop us from where we want to be is that leap of faith.

Are you ready to take that leap?

_____

_____

_____

_____

_____

_____

_____

_____

_____

_____

_____

_____

_____

Day 69

___ / ___ / ___

Look at the feelings chart to identify how you are feeling today.

How are you setting the tone in your relationships?

The way you treat yourself is the way people will treat you.

_____

_____

_____

_____

_____

_____

_____

_____

_____

_____

_____

_____

_____

_____

_____

_____

Day 70
__ / __ / __

How are you feeling today?

Look at the feelings chart to identify how you are feeling today.
If you are still breathing, there is room for change.
Tell yourself that when you start feeling like it's too late.

_____

_____

_____

_____

_____

_____

_____

_____

_____

_____

_____

_____

Look at the feelings chart to identify how you are feeling today.

Happiness starts with you.

What are you going to do daily to make sure you are truly happy?

_____

_____

_____

_____

_____

_____

_____

_____

_____

_____

_____

_____

_____

_____

_____

_____

_____

Day 72

___ / ___ / ___

Look at the feelings chart to identify how you are feeling today.

Each moment we have a choice.

We can continue to dwell on our past

or become the pioneer of our future.

What will you choose?

_____

_____

_____

_____

_____

_____

_____

_____

_____

_____

_____

_____

_____

Look at the feelings chart to identify how you are feeling today.
If you are looking for motivation to change, the fact that you are
not where you want to be in life should be enough motivation.

Day 74

___ / ___ / ___

Look at the feelings chart to identify how you are feeling today.

It's okay to have disagreement on issues.

Sometimes people have not seen things from

your perspective, so they may not understand.

It's important to remember this when you find yourself struggling with others.

_____

_____

_____

_____

_____

_____

_____

_____

_____

_____

_____

_____

_____

Look at the feelings chart to identify how you are feeling today.

Do you really know yourself?

If you know yourself, then you will not allow someone

to say something to you that causes you to react negatively.

Remember they are outside of you, which means that they should

not have power over what takes place inside of you.

_____

_____

_____

_____

_____

_____

_____

_____

_____

_____

_____

_____

_____

_____

_____

Day 76

___ / ___ / ___

Look at the feelings chart to identify how you are feeling today.
We create these walls in our head. We tell ourselves
we can't do things because of our past experiences.
Those walls may have helped you at one point in your life.
Now, they are hindering you from moving forward.
Today's the day to start breaking down those walls.

_____

_____

_____

_____

_____

_____

_____

_____

_____

_____

_____

_____

_____

_____

Day 77

___ / ___ / ___

Look at the feelings chart to identify how you are feeling today.

Do you have goals you want to accomplish?

Do you find yourself saying, "someday"?

Where is someday located on the calendar?

Step out your comfort zone and let today be the day you make it happen.

_____

_____

_____

_____

_____

_____

_____

_____

_____

_____

_____

_____

_____

_____

_____

_____

Day 78

__ / __ / __

Look at the feelings chart to identify how you are feeling today.
What we take in and who we surround
ourselves with will shape our mindset.
Are you surrounded by love and positivity?

_____
_____
_____
_____
_____
_____
_____
_____
_____
_____
_____
_____
_____
_____
_____

Day 79

___ / ___ / ___

Look at the feelings chart to identify how you are feeling today.

Do you know your worth?

It's important to know your value.

_____

_____

_____

_____

_____

_____

_____

_____

_____

_____

_____

_____

_____

_____

_____

Day 80
__ / __ / __

Look at the feelings chart to identify how you are feeling today.
It's important you do not get sidetracked
by people who are not on track.
Have you checked your circle lately?

_____

_____

_____

_____

_____

_____

_____

_____

_____

_____

_____

_____

_____

_____

_____

Day 81

___ / ___ / ___

Look at the feelings chart to identify how you are feeling today.
You will never change how people feel
about you or what they say about you.
What you can change is how you react toward them.

_____

_____

_____

_____

_____

_____

_____

_____

_____

_____

_____

_____

_____

_____

_____

_____

Day 82
__ / __ / __

Look at the feelings chart to identify how you are feeling today.

It's hard for us to heal because we struggle with forgiveness.

Have you forgiven yourself?

Forgiving yourself is so important.

Remember you are human.

_____
_____
_____
_____
_____
_____
_____
_____
_____
_____
_____
_____
_____

How are you feeling today?

Look at the feelings chart to identify how you are feeling today. Go ahead and make a decision. You're fixated on what could go wrong but, guess what, so many things could actually go right.

_____

_____

_____

_____

_____

_____

_____

_____

_____

_____

_____

_____

_____

_____

_____

_____

Day 84

___ / ___ / ___

Look at the feelings chart to identify how you are feeling today.

Are you wasting time trying to impress people?

Do what you love and love what you do.

_____

_____

_____

_____

_____

_____

_____

_____

_____

_____

_____

_____

_____

Day 85

___ / ___ / ___

Look at the feelings chart to identify how you are feeling today.

Everyone has the same 24 hours in a day.

What are you doing with your time?

Do you feel like you are being productive throughout the day?

_____

_____

_____

_____

_____

_____

_____

_____

_____

_____

_____

_____

_____

_____

_____

_____

Day 86

__ / __ / __

Look at the feelings chart to identify how you are feeling today.
It is important that you are kind to yourself
because you are listening and acting on your thoughts.
What are some ways you can treat yourself better?

_____

_____

_____

_____

_____

_____

_____

_____

_____

_____

_____

_____

Look at the feelings chart to identify how you are feeling today.

You have something you are trying to achieve?

You may have to step out of your comfort zone to make it happen.

_____
_____
_____
_____
_____
_____
_____
_____
_____
_____
_____
_____
_____
_____
_____
_____

Day 88

___ / ___ / ___

Look at the feelings chart to identify how you are feeling today.
If you suppress the parts of you that you do not
want to see, it can leave you feeling unbalanced.
Try looking at your entire self.

_____

_____

_____

_____

_____

_____

_____

_____

_____

_____

_____

_____

_____

Day 89

___ / ___ / ___

Look at the feelings chart to identify how you are feeling today.
Do you notice negative thoughts sneaking in your mindset?
If you are aware of them, you can try and reframe them.

Day 90

___ / ___ / ___

Do you know what the future holds?

Why should you spend it worrying?

It is important to stay mindful on what and how you are thinking.

_____

_____

_____

_____

_____

_____

_____

_____

_____

_____

_____

_____

_____

_____

How are you feeling today?

Do you notice yourself having negative thoughts?
If you are aware of them, you can try to
counter them with something positive.

_____

_____

_____

_____

_____

_____

_____

_____

_____

_____

_____

_____

_____

_____

_____

Day 92
___ / ___ / ___

Do not let your past dictate your future.
Learn from your past, forgive yourself
and others that may have hurt you.

Day 93

__ / __ / __

How are you moving through life?

Do you find yourself rushing?

If so, why? What are you trying to achieve?

_____

_____

_____

_____

_____

_____

_____

_____

_____

_____

_____

_____

_____

_____

Day 94

___ / ___ / ___

We are conditioned to be doing what everyone else is doing.

Try living an intentional life.

Do you feel you have been intentional about doing what's best for you?

If not, how can you be more intentional?

_____

_____

_____

_____

_____

_____

_____

_____

_____

_____

_____

_____

_____

Day 95
__ / __ / __

Do you feel like the people in your life are adding value?
Take some time to evaluate how the
people in your life are treating you.
Are the relationships reciprocal?

_____

_____

_____

_____

_____

_____

_____

_____

_____

_____

_____

_____

_____

_____

_____

Day 96

__ / __ / __

What did you do yesterday that led you
towards the direction of your goal?
If the answer is nothing, plan on doing something this week.

_____

_____

_____

_____

_____

_____

_____

_____

_____

_____

_____

_____

_____

_____

Day 97

___ / ___ / ___

If you find yourself struggling with other
people's perspectives, understand that everyone
is different and has different stories to tell.
Sometimes you just have to agree to disagree.

_____
_____
_____
_____
_____
_____
_____
_____
_____
_____
_____
_____
_____
_____
_____
_____

Day 98
__ / __ / __

One of the greatest things you can do for
yourself is learn who you really are.
When you learn who you are, no one can take that away.
Who are you?

_____

_____

_____

_____

_____

_____

_____

_____

_____

_____

_____

_____

_____

Day 99

___ / ___ / ___

Sometimes we build walls in our head that
prohibit us from growing in life.
It is important to think about the barriers to our growth.
What mental walls have you built?
It is important that we recognize and stay mindful of the things that hold us back.

_____

_____

_____

_____

_____

_____

_____

_____

_____

_____

_____

_____

_____

_____

_____

Day 100

___ / ___ / ___

Forgiving yourself is important.

You are human.

If you are holding on to something you have done,

learn how to forgive yourself. It's necessary for growth.

_____

_____

_____

_____

_____

_____

_____

_____

_____

_____

_____

_____

_____

Day 101

___ / ___ / ___

Growth is so necessary. If you are growing your alive. Sometimes
we feel dead inside because we are afraid of change.
If you want to go to higher heights, you have to grow.
Do not allow fear of the unknown stop you from achieving your goals

_____

_____

_____

_____

_____

_____

_____

_____

_____

_____

_____

_____

_____

_____

_____

_____

Day 102
___ / ___ / ___

Life is too short not to be happy. Happiness starts on the inside.

_____

_____

_____

_____

_____

_____

_____

_____

_____

_____

_____

_____

_____

How are you feeling today?

We miss out on life when we are worrying about the future.

Are you living in the moment?

_____
_____
_____
_____
_____
_____
_____
_____
_____
_____
_____
_____
_____
_____
_____
_____

Day 104

___ / ___ / ___

Sometimes you may not feel like doing what
you have to do to reach your goal.
It is important to push pass that feeling and think of
the results that you will gain when you achieve your goal.
You can do this.
You just have to have the faith to believe in yourself.

_____

_____

_____

_____

_____

_____

_____

_____

_____

_____

_____

_____

_____

_____

Day 105

___ / ___ / ___

We have goals, we make plans, but we fail to execute.

Use what you can and just do it.

Its time to start making your goals a reality.

Day 106
__ / __ / __

Did you know that faith drives out fear?
In order to have faith, it's important you are
feeding your faith. If you are not being intentional
on feeding your faith, then fear will always win.

_____

_____

_____

_____

_____

_____

_____

_____

_____

_____

_____

_____

Do you have something you are trying to accomplish but find yourself stuck? You have to make a commitment and be consistent.

Day 108

__ / __ / __

Think about how a tree started.

It was once a seed.

Everything doesn't start big.

Day 109

__ / __ / __

Start focusing on you and take it one day at a time

_____
_____
_____
_____
_____
_____
_____
_____
_____
_____
_____
_____
_____
_____
_____
_____

Day 110
__ / __ / __

Letting go is so hard but, waiting can be even
harder. Ask yourself, "What do I deserve?"
You deserve the best! You have to have the faith to believe that.

_____

_____

_____

_____

_____

_____

_____

_____

_____

_____

_____

_____

_____

Look at what you have now to achieve your goal.
Just because it's not everything you want, doesn't
mean you can't use what you have in front of you.
It starts with a paper and pen. Start writing your vision down.

Day 112

___/___/___

Do not allow the people who hate on you discourage you.

You can think of them as your motivator.

You can't change a hater.

_____

_____

_____

_____

_____

_____

_____

_____

_____

_____

_____

_____

_____

Day 113
__/ __ / __

We all have choices. We can be ourselves or we
can be who we think others want us to be.
Every morning, choose to be you.
It feels so good to just wake up and be you.
Do you feel like you are being true to yourself?

Day 114

__ / __ / __

Just because something did not work
out it does not mean it's over.
Look at the things you call failures as life lessons.
Change your perspective.

How are you feeling today?

_____

_____

_____

_____

_____

_____

_____

_____

_____

_____

_____

_____

Day 115

__ / __ / __

It's time you stop worrying about how others feel about you.
You can't stop someone from judging you.
If you want to stop caring about being judged, you have to
learn yourself and become authentic. When you are living YOUR life,
and being authentic, no one can ever take that away from you..

_____

_____

_____

_____

_____

_____

_____

_____

_____

_____

_____

_____

_____

_____

_____

_____

_____

Day 116

___ / ___ / ___

It is important to tell yourself each day, "One day at a time."
Life is a journey, not a race.

_____

_____

_____

_____

_____

_____

_____

_____

_____

_____

_____

_____

_____

_____

Self-care is a major part of success.

Learn how to set boundaries and be consistent.

_____

_____

_____

_____

_____

_____

_____

_____

_____

_____

_____

_____

_____

_____

_____

_____

Day 118

__ / __ / __

It is important that you stop comparing
yourself to other people and look in the mirror to
compare yourself to who you were yesterday.
Always strive for a better you.

_____

_____

_____

_____

_____

_____

_____

_____

_____

_____

_____

_____

How are you feeling today?

If you can be intentional on distancing yourself from the negativity, you will find yourself in a different space mentally.

Day 120
__ / __ / __

Stop looking at yourself in a negative way because
you are different. Being different is okay.

_____

_____

_____

_____

_____

_____

_____

_____

_____

_____

_____

_____

_____

_____

There is room in life for everyone to win.

Everything is not a competition.

Your only competition should be a better version of you.

Day 122

___ / ___ / ___

Stop letting fear control you.
Try turning fear into hope.

_____

_____

_____

_____

_____

_____

_____

_____

_____

_____

_____

_____

_____

How are you feeling today?

If what you are doing isn't working, why
not try something different?
Anything you need to try differently?

_____
_____
_____
_____
_____
_____
_____
_____
_____
_____
_____
_____
_____
_____
_____
_____
_____

Day 124

__ / __ / __

Stop saying, "one day I will do it" and just make it happen today.
You can make it happen by writing a realistic plan for yourself.

_____

_____

_____

_____

_____

_____

_____

_____

_____

_____

_____

_____

_____

_____

How are you feeling today?

Do you know who you are?
We are conditioned to be who society says we should be.
If you feel you do not know who you are,
you can try letting go of societal norms.

_____
_____
_____
_____
_____
_____
_____
_____
_____
_____
_____
_____
_____
_____
_____
_____

Day 126
___/___/___

It is important that we learn the difference
between our wants and our needs.
Sometimes the things that we hold on to
(wants) keep us from receiving what we need.

_____

_____

_____

_____

_____

_____

_____

_____

_____

_____

_____

_____

_____

_____

_____

_____

Day 127
___ / ___ / ___

Sometimes you may wonder if you are winning in life.
If you ask yourself this question, often it's because you continue
to focus on the things you lack and forget to embrace what you have.

_____

_____

_____

_____

_____

_____

_____

_____

_____

_____

_____

_____

_____

_____

Day 128

___ / ___ / ___

We all have choices.

It is time you start taking responsibility for your actions.

Do you feel like you are taking responsibility for your actions?

Setting boundaries is an important life skill.
Do you feel like you are setting boundaries to take care of yourself?
If not, how can you start setting boundaries today?

_____
_____
_____
_____
_____
_____
_____
_____
_____
_____
_____
_____
_____
_____
_____
_____

Day 130
__ / __ / __

Imagine how intentional your life can be if
you start thinking before you act.

_____
_____
_____
_____
_____
_____
_____
_____
_____
_____
_____
_____
_____

Day 131

__ / __ / __

Do you find yourself stressing over things that are not in your control? If you do not have control over it, learn how to let it go.

_____

_____

_____

_____

_____

_____

_____

_____

_____

_____

_____

_____

_____

_____

_____

Day 132

__ / __ / __

Stop dreaming about what you want to do.

Just go out and do it.

Are you doing what you need to do to make your dreams come true?

_____

_____

_____

_____

_____

_____

_____

_____

_____

_____

_____

_____

_____

_____

_____

_____

Day 133

___ / ___ / ___

It is important that you stop looking for validation.
If you have no one rooting you on, learn
how to be your biggest motivator.

_____

_____

_____

_____

_____

_____

_____

_____

_____

_____

_____

_____

_____

_____

Day 134

___ / ___ / ___

Know yourself and embrace your uniqueness.

Day 135

___ / ___ / ___

Is your life being controlled by internal wounds from your past?
It is important that you analyze yourself and your decisions.

_____
_____
_____
_____
_____
_____
_____
_____
_____
_____
_____
_____
_____
_____
_____
_____

Day 136

___ / ___ / ___

Sometimes we are worrying so much that we
forget to start working on our goals.
Get out of your head and start making your goals happen.

_____

_____

_____

_____

_____

_____

_____

_____

_____

_____

_____

_____

How are you feeling today?

___ / ___ / ___

Your relationships should be reciprocal.
Make sure you are not the only one giving.

_____
_____
_____
_____
_____
_____
_____
_____
_____
_____
_____
_____
_____
_____
_____
_____

Day 138

__/__/__

How are you feeling today?

Consistency and commitment are a major key to success.

Have you experienced trauma?

If you are dealing with the trauma, you are constantly triggered.

Dealing with trauma allows you to maintain control over your mind.

_____

_____

_____

_____

_____

_____

_____

_____

_____

_____

_____

_____

_____

_____

Day 140

___ / ___ / ___

Life doesn't always happen like we expect it to happen.

I challenge you to let go of expectations.

If you do that, you can live in the moment.

_____

_____

_____

_____

_____

_____

_____

_____

_____

_____

_____

_____

_____

How are you feeling today?

If you have goals that you are trying to accomplish,
being consistent is a major key.

_____
_____
_____
_____
_____
_____
_____
_____
_____
_____
_____
_____
_____
_____
_____

Day 142

___ / ___ / ___

Did you know that you matter?

Sometimes you may feel drained.

Sometimes it's due to the fact that you are not putting yourself first.

Are you taking care of yourself everyday?

_____

_____

_____

_____

_____

_____

_____

_____

_____

_____

_____

_____

Day 143

___ / ___ / ___

Because we can pride ourselves as being strong, we fail to
realize how our broken pieces in life have hindered us.
We continue to grow physically, but mentally we are stuck.
Do you find yourself stuck?

_____

_____

_____

_____

_____

_____

_____

_____

_____

_____

_____

_____

_____

_____

_____

_____

Day 144
___ / ___ / ___

Forgiveness does not excuse what happened to you.
Forgiveness will allow you to move forward in life.

How are you feeling today?

_____
_____
_____
_____
_____
_____
_____
_____
_____
_____
_____
_____
_____

Day 145

___ / ___ / ___

Do you love yourself?
Forgive yourself for past mistakes.
This is an important part of growth.

Day 146
__ / __ / __

Feeling stuck in life?

If yes, have you accepted where you are in life.

Acceptance is acknowledging your current reality.

If it's not where you want to be, you can plan to make changes in your life.

You have to be intentional for the plan to work.

_____

_____

_____

_____

_____

_____

_____

_____

_____

_____

_____

_____

_____

How do you define being whole?
Being whole does not mean you are perfect.
It simply means accepting who you are and
learning to be content with it. If it's not who you want to be,
you can work on achieving certain goals for yourself.

_____

_____

_____

_____

_____

_____

_____

_____

_____

_____

_____

_____

_____

_____

_____

_____

Day 148

___ / ___ / ___

Keep pushing forward.

Having hope is so necessary in life.

If what you are doing is not working, it is
important to try something different.

_____
_____
_____
_____
_____
_____
_____
_____
_____
_____
_____
_____
_____
_____
_____
_____

Day 150

___ / ___ / ___

Even through your darkest days, you must fight hard
to remind yourself after the rain there is a rainbow.

How are you feeling today?

Day 151
___ / ___ / ___

Authenticity is key.
Be yourself so no one can ever take that away from you.

Day 152
__ / __ / __

What and whom are you inviting in your life?

Make sure you are constantly assessing the way you treat yourself.

You deserve the best.

_____

_____

_____

_____

_____

_____

_____

_____

_____

_____

_____

_____

_____

_____

How are you feeling today?

Day 153
__ / __ / __

You have a purpose in life.

_____
_____
_____
_____
_____
_____
_____
_____
_____
_____
_____
_____
_____
_____
_____
_____
_____

Day 154
__ / __ / __

Imagine what could happen if we started to highlight our joys?
In this very moment, right now it's important
to focus on inner peace and happiness.

How are you feeling today?

You may not be here tomorrow.
Why waste your energy living in fear?

Day 156

___ / ___ / ___

What is more important to you?

Your material possessions or your inner peace and happiness?

_____

_____

_____

_____

_____

_____

_____

_____

_____

_____

_____

_____

_____

_____

Day 157
__ / __ / __

You may be your own hinderance to growing to your full potential.
Can you think of areas where you are
hindering yourself from growing?

_____

_____

_____

_____

_____

_____

_____

_____

_____

_____

_____

_____

_____

_____

_____

_____

Day 158

___ / ___ / ___

Just because you are right, doesn't mean
the other person is wrong.
It is important you understand that there are
people who may have different life experiences.
Take that into account when a disagreement takes place.

Did you know that you will repeat the things you do not repair?

What areas in your life need repairs?

Day 160
__ / __ / __

Are you using band aids to deal with your problems in life?

It's important to not cover up our problems with temporary fixes.

What band aids are you using in life.

_____

_____

_____

_____

_____

_____

_____

_____

_____

_____

_____

_____

_____

_____

_____

How are you feeling today?

We miss out on life when we worry about the future.

Try living in the moment.

Day 162

__ / __ / __

What if I told you that your past does not have to keep you stuck?

You can keep going.

You are destined for greatness.

You just must have the faith to believe that.

_____

_____

_____

_____

_____

_____

_____

_____

_____

_____

_____

_____

_____

_____

How are you feeling today?

Life is too short for dreams.
Get up, get out and make memories.

Day 164

___/___/___

If you are trying to create a positive life style,
do not be afraid of losing people.
Be afraid of losing yourself.

_____

_____

_____

_____

_____

_____

_____

_____

_____

_____

_____

_____

_____

Having low self-esteem can hinder you from moving forward.
How do you really feel about yourself?
If you feel like your esteem is low, continue
challenging yourself to speak positive over your life.

_____
_____
_____
_____
_____
_____
_____
_____
_____
_____
_____
_____
_____
_____
_____
_____

Day 166

___ / ___ / ___

How do you start your day?

Do you look on social media first thing in the morning?

Try starting it with meditation.

Create time to start your day off right.

_____

_____

_____

_____

_____

_____

_____

_____

_____

_____

_____

_____

Day 167

___ / ___ / ___

If you are in a relationship; Is knowing yourself important?
If not, then its important you make it a
priority to get to know yourself.

_____

_____

_____

_____

_____

_____

_____

_____

_____

_____

_____

_____

_____

_____

_____

Day 168
___/___/___

Forgiveness is hard but necessary.
If we can't forgive, we create a wall around our heart
that will block us from receiving and spreading love.

_____
_____
_____
_____
_____
_____
_____
_____
_____
_____
_____
_____
_____
_____

Day 169

___/___/___

If you find yourself in a negative cycle in life, you
must first learn how to be conscious and present.
Once you are present and see the affects it has
on you, you can plan to make concrete changes.

_____

_____

_____

_____

_____

_____

_____

_____

_____

_____

_____

_____

_____

_____

_____

Day 170
__/__/__

In life, we tend to suffer because we are more
concerned about what we look like on the outside
and not concerned about what's going on internally.

_____

_____

_____

_____

_____

_____

_____

_____

_____

_____

_____

_____

_____

_____

Day 171

___ / ___ / ___

Make sure you are constantly doing self-assessments
and taking responsibility for your actions.

Day 172
___ / ___ / ___

Try living in the now.

If you do that, you can focus on the today.

How are you feeling today?

If not now, then when?
Time waits for nobody.
What are you putting off doing?
Make plans today.

Day 174
___/___/___

Are you in a relationship and feeling unhappy?
If you are not happy with who you are outside of a relationship,
how do you expect to find happiness in someone else?

_____
_____
_____
_____
_____
_____
_____
_____
_____
_____
_____
_____
_____

How much time are you really investing in yourself?
We invest in the things we care about.
Make sure your needs are being met.

_____

_____

_____

_____

_____

_____

_____

_____

_____

_____

_____

_____

_____

_____

_____

_____

Day 176

___/___/___

As children, we had no control over our environment.

As an adult, we can create the environment

in which we want to see ourselves.

This means letting go of negative energy and negative people.

_____

_____

_____

_____

_____

_____

_____

_____

_____

_____

_____

_____

Are you feeling stuck and need motivation?

Life is short.

Let that marinate because time waits for no one.

Day 178

___ / ___ / ___

Are you making every moment count?
If the answer is no, start being intentional
about living in the present.

You owe yourself the same love you give to other people.
You deserve the best and you are worthy.

Day 180

___/___/___

If we start agreeing to disagree, it can honor
our differences while offering a solution.

How are you feeling today?

_____

_____

_____

_____

_____

_____

_____

_____

_____

_____

_____

_____

_____

_____

How are you feeling today?

Do you find yourself worrying all the time?
If yes, ask yourself, "Do I have control over it?"
If the answer is no, learn how to let it go.

_____
_____
_____
_____
_____
_____
_____
_____
_____
_____
_____
_____
_____
_____
_____

Day 182

__/__/__

How are you feeling today?

How do you move forward if you continue to look back?

How are you feeling today?

What is on your to do list today?

Living in the moment should always be on your to do list.

You are now halfway through the journal. You will now be asked the same question or statement from the beginning. The purpose is to see how your thoughts have changed through the journaling process.

Because you may not be working with a therapist, I wanted to give you a way of identifying the changes being made. If you are seeing a therapist or thinking about seeing a therapist, this is a perfect tool to use to process your emotions.

Day 184

___ / ___ / ___

Did you know that stigma continues to stop us from checking
in about our mental health? Would you wait to bandage your
bleeding finger? Why do you wait to check in with yourself?
How are you really doing? It's important to be honest with yourself.

_____
_____
_____
_____
_____
_____
_____
_____
_____
_____
_____
_____
_____
_____
_____
_____

See your progress, check how you answered this question on Day 1

Day 185

__ / __ / __

You must make yourself a priority.

You make that happen by deciding to put YOU first.

Are you putting yourself first?

_____

_____

_____

_____

_____

_____

_____

_____

_____

_____

_____

_____

_____

_____

_____

See your progress, check how you answered this question on Day 2

Your actions come from how you feel, and
feelings come from your thoughts.
If you want to change your behaviors, it's
important to understand your thoughts.

_____

_____

_____

_____

_____

_____

_____

_____

_____

_____

_____

_____

_____

_____

_____

_____

See your progress, check how you answered this question on Day 3

Day 187

___ / ___ / ___

It's okay to say, "I'm not okay." If you want to heal, its
important you start being honest with yourself.
You are human life is a journey.

_____

_____

_____

_____

_____

_____

_____

_____

_____

_____

_____

_____

_____

See your progress, check how you answered this question on Day 4

Day 188

___/___/___

Angry, frustrated, sad, confused are all normal emotions to have during hard times. How you handle these emotions is so important. Do you feel you have control over your emotions?

_____
_____
_____
_____
_____
_____
_____
_____
_____
_____
_____
_____
_____
_____
_____
_____

See your progress, check how you answered this question on Day 5

Day 189

___ / ___ / ___

Stay mindful on the impact of negative moments in your life. Sometimes negative moments can impact us in a negative way. Make sure you have HEALTHY outlets to deal with it. What healthy outlets do you have?

_____

_____

_____

_____

_____

_____

_____

_____

_____

_____

_____

_____

_____

_____

_____

See your progress, check how you answered this question on Day 6

Sometimes we procrastinate and say, "maybe tomorrow".
We wait to make amends with people; we wait to
start our goals; we wait to really live our lives.
It's important to understand that tomorrow may never come.
Knowing this fact should be motivation to start really living in the NOW.

See your progress, check how you answered this question on Day 7

Day 191

___ / ___ / ___

Sometimes we are where we are in life
because we do not have an open mind.
We are not open to new opportunities, ways of dealing with emotions
or even listening to advice. When your mind is closed, nothing can leave or go
in. Life is too short to keep doing the same thing getting the same result.

_____

_____

_____

_____

_____

_____

_____

_____

_____

_____

_____

_____

_____

See your progress, check how you answered this question on Day 8

Even though the journey of self-awareness and
loving yourself can be lonely, doing this will allow
you mental stability and emotional freedom.

See your progress, check how you answered this question on Day 9

Day 193

___ / ___ / ___

Life is a journey full of ups and downs.

We mastered dealing with good times,

but we ignore the hard times.

It's hard to live a balanced life when you are ignoring parts of yourself.

_____

_____

_____

_____

_____

_____

_____

_____

_____

_____

_____

_____

_____

See your progress, check how you answered this question on Day 10

Stop asking yourself, "why do people hurt me?" Reframe
the question to, "Why am I allowing people to hurt me?"
When you reframe the question, it helps you feel
empowered and gives you control to make healthy choices.

_____

_____

_____

_____

_____

_____

_____

_____

_____

_____

_____

_____

_____

_____

_____

_____

See your progress, check how you answered this question on Day 11

Day 195

__/__/__

Are you waiting for validation to make your next move?
To people out there with no support, understand you can do this.
You have more power than you think, you
have to start having faith to believe that.

_____

_____

_____

_____

_____

_____

_____

_____

_____

_____

_____

_____

_____

_____

See your progress, check how you answered this question on Day 12

The best things in life are the moments.
Moments are important decisions and events in your life.
It's time we create beautiful moments that will last a life time.
Are you creating moments?

See your progress, check how you answered this question on Day 13

Day 197

__ / __ / __

Write down some positive changes you can make in your life.
Think of some things you can change today.

How are you feeling today?

_____

_____

_____

_____

_____

_____

_____

_____

_____

_____

_____

_____

_____

_____

_____

See your progress, check how you answered this question on Day 14

Change starts with you.
Are you intentionally making positive changes?
Did you implement any changes you wrote down on Day 14?

_____

_____

_____

_____

_____

_____

_____

_____

_____

_____

_____

_____

_____

_____

_____

_____

See your progress, check how you answered this question on Day 15

Day 199

___ / ___ / ___

Are you creating a life that feels good on the inside
and not one that just looks good on the outside?

See your progress, check how you answered this question on Day 16

How are you feeling today?

Learn how to reframe how you speak about yourself.
Speaking positive over your life is so necessary.
Sometimes we have internal thoughts we are not aware of.
Listen to how you speak about yourself.
Are you being kind to yourself?

See your progress, check how you answered this question on Day 17

Day 201
__ / __ / __

Stigma continues to stop people from asking for help.

Would you be ashamed if you cut your finger and it was bleeding?

If you feel you need mental health support, it is important you ask.

Life is too short to continue suffering in silence.

_____

_____

_____

_____

_____

_____

_____

_____

_____

_____

_____

_____

_____

_____

See your progress, check how you answered this question on Day 18

Often, people tell themselves that when they get a
job or more money they will be happy. For example,
some people are waiting for a promotion at their job.
People will say, "Once I become a manager, I will be happy." We plan for
happiness as a future event. How would you describe happiness?

_____

_____

_____

_____

_____

_____

_____

_____

_____

_____

_____

_____

_____

_____

_____

See your progress, check how you answered this question on Day 19

Day 203

___ / ___ / ___

Many people think they are not happy when they are not in a
relationship. As humans we yearn for someone to love us.
Do you love yourself? You can't depend
or look for love solely in other people.
Loving yourself is so important.

_____

_____

_____

_____

_____

_____

_____

_____

_____

_____

_____

_____

_____

_____

_____

See your progress, check how you answered this question on Day 20

Day 204
__ / __ / __

I once heard someone say, "normal is just a dial on the washing machine." It's important you stop looking at yourself negatively because you are different from everyone else. Being different is okay. You are unique and wonderfully made. Don't forget that.

See your progress, check how you answered this question on Day 21

Day 205
__/__/__

Did you know that you are AMAZING?

Do you feel amazing?

Speaking positively about yourself is very important.

Try saying it to yourself now. "I am Amazing."

_____
_____
_____
_____
_____
_____
_____
_____
_____
_____
_____
_____
_____
_____

See your progress, check how you answered this question on Day 22

Did you know there are 86,200 seconds in a day?

Are you making each one count?

Day 207
__ / __ / __

If you focus on the good things that are happening in
your life, it can change the way you view your life.
What do you find yourself focusing on?

_____
_____
_____
_____
_____
_____
_____
_____
_____
_____
_____
_____
_____
_____

See your progress, check how you answered this question on Day 24

People will treat you how you allow them to treat you. Are
the people in your life kind and supportive to you?

_____

_____

_____

_____

_____

_____

_____

_____

_____

_____

_____

_____

_____

_____

_____

See your progress, check how you answered this question on Day 25

Day 209

___/___/___

Get rid of the negative people in your life. We continue
to allow them back in our lives. It's time to learn how
to stop the negative cycle so that you can grow.
Always check the people that are in your circle.

_____

_____

_____

_____

_____

_____

_____

_____

_____

_____

_____

_____

_____

See your progress, check how you answered this question on Day 26

Are you waiting for validation? Do you wait for
someone to breathe? We breathe alone and if you are
someone who does not have people validating you, keep
going. Stop waiting for someone to say keep going or good job.
Learn how to motivate yourself.

_____

_____

_____

_____

_____

_____

_____

_____

_____

_____

_____

_____

_____

_____

_____

See your progress, check how you answered this question on Day 27

Day 211

___ / ___ / ___

Are you collecting moments or things? Which
do you cherish the most? It's time we create
beautiful moments that will last a lifetime.

_____

_____

_____

_____

_____

_____

_____

_____

_____

_____

_____

_____

_____

See your progress, check how you answered this question on Day 28

Are you struggling with trying to make positive
changes in your life? What can you start doing
today to make a positive impact on your life?

_____
_____
_____
_____
_____
_____
_____
_____
_____
_____
_____
_____
_____
_____
_____
_____

See your progress, check how you answered this question on Day 29

Day 213

___ / ___ / ___

Do you believe in yourself?

_____
_____
_____
_____
_____
_____
_____
_____
_____
_____
_____
_____
_____
_____
_____

See your progress, check how you answered this question on Day 30

Did you know that there is room in life for everyone to win?
Everything is not a competition.
Make sure you focus on yourself and your goals.
We can all bloom together.

_____

_____

_____

_____

_____

_____

_____

_____

_____

_____

_____

_____

_____

_____

_____

_____

_____

See your progress, check how you answered this question on Day 31

Day 215

___/___/___

What do you say about yourself? If you find yourself speaking negative, learn how to reframe how you speak about yourself. Speaking positive over your life is so necessary.

_____

_____

_____

_____

_____

_____

_____

_____

_____

_____

_____

_____

_____

See your progress, check how you answered this question on Day 32

How are you feeling today?

Do you find yourself focused on the future?

Forget about the future because it's not here.

Stop wasting time worrying; it can continue to cause anxiety in your life.

Leave the future for the future.

See your progress, check how you answered this question on Day 33

Day 217

___ / ___ / ___

Knowing your triggers is an important part of dealing with life.
Do you know the things in your life that hinder
you from moving forward with your goals?
If you say no, start being mindful throughout the day of
how people, things and situations affect you.

_____
_____
_____
_____
_____
_____
_____
_____
_____
_____
_____
_____
_____
_____

See your progress, check how you answered this question on Day 34

today. Life can feel hard at times. The only thing we can do is learn how to truly live and be prepared to deal with the curve balls that are being thrown at us. How do you deal with life?

_____

_____

_____

_____

_____

_____

_____

_____

_____

_____

_____

_____

_____

_____

_____

See your progress, check how you answered this question on Day 35

Day 219
__ / __ / __

You have more power than you realize.

You just have to have the faith to believe that.

Do you believe in yourself?

_____

_____

_____

_____

_____

_____

_____

_____

_____

_____

_____

_____

_____

See your progress, check how you answered this question on Day 36

How are you feeling today?

You are okay. Things will get better. You may not believe that
right now but it's important to speak positive over your life.

_____
_____
_____
_____
_____
_____
_____
_____
_____
_____
_____
_____
_____
_____
_____
_____
_____

See your progress, check how you answered this question on Day 37

Day 221

___ / ___ / ___

"I can do this."

Yes, you can absolutely do this.

Never let anyone tell you otherwise.

_____

_____

_____

_____

_____

_____

_____

_____

_____

_____

_____

_____

_____

_____

See your progress, check how you answered this question on Day 38

How are you feeling today?

Running away from your problems will not solve anything.
The only way to deal with internal pain is to deal with it.
Healing starts from the inside.

_____
_____
_____
_____
_____
_____
_____
_____
_____
_____
_____
_____
_____
_____

See your progress, check how you answered this question on Day 39

Day 223
__ / __ / __

Be conscious of what is happening to you mentally.
When you are conscious of it, it's easier to cope
with the uncomfortable feelings you may have.

_____

_____

_____

_____

_____

_____

_____

_____

_____

_____

_____

_____

_____

See your progress, check how you answered this question on Day 40

Day 224
___ / ___ / ___

It's okay to have emotions and feelings because you are human.
It's important you learn how to deal with
those emotions in a healthy way.
How are you dealing with your emotions?

See your progress, check how you answered this question on Day 41

Day 225

___ / ___ / ___

Did you know you can end up being a
prisoner when you do not forgive?
You become locked inside the anger or hatred.
Do you find yourself holding anger and hate in your heart for someone?
If you answer yes, how is that helping you?

_____
_____
_____
_____
_____
_____
_____
_____
_____
_____
_____
_____
_____

See your progress, check how you answered this question on Day 42

Tell yourself that life is worth living.
Continue to say it and you will believe it.
There is something powerful about having a
positive narrative about your life and destiny.

Day 227

___ / ___ / ___

Do you feel like you are searching for happiness?

Have you thought about what happiness means to you?

How do you expect you find it?

_____

_____

_____

_____

_____

_____

_____

_____

_____

_____

_____

_____

_____

See your progress, check how you answered this question on Day 44

How are you feeling today?

Look in the mirror and say, "I love you."
Work on being in love with you.

_____
_____
_____
_____
_____
_____
_____
_____
_____
_____
_____
_____
_____
_____
_____
_____
_____

See your progress, check how you answered this question on Day 45

Day 229
__/__/__

When you are sad and alone, your mind can lead you to believe
that your current feelings are permanent.
It is important to understand that feelings are temporary.

_____

_____

_____

_____

_____

_____

_____

_____

_____

_____

_____

_____

_____

_____

See your progress, check how you answered this question on Day 46

People continue to search for balance in life and come up empty.
The problem is that you have to CREATE
a balance life to make it happen.

See your progress, check how you answered this question on Day 47

Day 231

__ / __ / __

Mourn the loss of the life you wanted.

Even if you are not where you want to be, accept where you are and work on a plan to change.

See your progress, check how you answered this question on Day 48

Do you find yourself rushing through life?
What are you rushing for?

_____

_____

_____

_____

_____

_____

_____

_____

_____

_____

_____

_____

_____

_____

_____

See your progress, check how you answered this question on Day 49

Day 233
__ / __ / __

Do you feel like you are being yourself?
If not, why are you living a filtered life?
Why not just be you?

_____
_____
_____
_____
_____
_____
_____
_____
_____
_____
_____
_____
_____
_____
_____
_____

See your progress, check how you answered this question on Day 50

Self-care is important.
Are you taking care of everyone else?
Life is to short not to take care of yourself.

_____

_____

_____

_____

_____

_____

_____

_____

_____

_____

_____

_____

_____

_____

_____

_____

See your progress, check how you answered this question on Day 51

Day 235

___ / ___ / ___

When you dwell on the past and worry about
the future, you miss out on NOW.
What motto do you live by?

See your progress, check how you answered this question on Day 52

Day 236
___ / ___ / ___

Being intentional is important.
We are intentional about getting dressed and brushing our teeth.
Are you intentional on taking care of your mental health?

See your progress, check how you answered this question on Day 53

Day 237

___/___/___

Check your circle. Are your relationships reciprocal?
Do you find yourself always giving of yourself
and not getting anything in return?

See your progress, check how you answered this question on Day 54

We spend too much time on social media and on our phones.
If you feel disconnected from your kids, partner and
yourself, you can try taking a break from social media.
This is so necessary.

Day 239

___ / ___ / ___

Do you have goals you want to accomplish?
Consistency and commitment is important.
Work on it even when you don't feel like it.

How are you feeling today?

_____

_____

_____

_____

_____

_____

_____

_____

_____

_____

_____

_____

See your progress, check how you answered this question on Day 56

Day 240

___ / ___ / ___

'I will do what's best for me." Say that to yourself.

_____

_____

_____

_____

_____

_____

_____

_____

_____

_____

_____

_____

_____

_____

See your progress, check how you answered this question on Day 57

Day 241

___ / ___ / ___

It's important to live in the present moment
because you can never get it back.
Do you feel like you are living in the present moment?

_____

_____

_____

_____

_____

_____

_____

_____

_____

_____

_____

_____

_____

_____

See your progress, check how you answered this question on Day 58

Day 242

___ / ___ / ___

People may not understand you and that's okay.
It's important that you are not allowing
other people to get inside your head.
They may never understand you.

_____

_____

_____

_____

_____

_____

_____

_____

_____

_____

_____

_____

_____

_____

See your progress, check how you answered this question on Day 59

Day 243

___ / ___ / ___

It is important that we have a positive narrative about ourselves.

Thinking positive feels better than thinking negative.

Try saying 3 positive things about yourself each day.

_____

_____

_____

_____

_____

_____

_____

_____

_____

_____

_____

_____

_____

_____

See your progress, check how you answered this question on Day 60

It is important you recognize the areas of
your life you can improve on.
What areas of your life can you start working on.

_____

_____

_____

_____

_____

_____

_____

_____

_____

_____

_____

_____

_____

_____

_____

_____

See your progress, check how you answered this question on Day 61

Day 245

__ / __ / __

Did you know that everyone does things at their own pace?
Just because it may have taken you longer to
complete something does not mean you failed.
Remember that.

_____

_____

_____

_____

_____

_____

_____

_____

_____

_____

_____

_____

_____

See your progress, check how you answered this question on Day 62

How are you feeling today?

Do you want to stop the negative cycles in your life?
It's important we recognize what is causing it.
We have to learn how to heal from our past.

_____

_____

_____

_____

_____

_____

_____

_____

_____

_____

_____

_____

_____

_____

_____

See your progress, check how you answered this question on Day 63

Day 247

___/___/___

Speaking positive and writing down how you want to
change is a great start. The next step to change is action. Do
you feel like you are actively trying to live an intentional life?

_____

_____

_____

_____

_____

_____

_____

_____

_____

_____

_____

_____

_____

_____

See your progress, check how you answered this question on Day 64

Day 248

___ / ___ / ___

Sometimes we allow what other people do
to have a negative effect on us.
Why do you allow people to control
what takes place with your emotions?

See your progress, check how you answered this question on Day 65

Day 249

___ / ___ / ___

We make time for things we care about. How
much do you care about yourself?
Are you making time to take care of you?

_____

_____

_____

_____

_____

_____

_____

_____

_____

_____

_____

_____

_____

_____

_____

See your progress, check how you answered this question on Day 66

Day 250

___ / ___ / ___

We say to ourselves, "Tomorrow, I'll do it or "one day I'll do it."

Why not make a plan to start today?

Time waits for no one.

_____

_____

_____

_____

_____

_____

_____

_____

_____

_____

_____

_____

_____

_____

_____

See your progress, check how you answered this question on Day 67

Day 251

__/__/__

You may not be where you want to be in life; that's okay.
What tends to stop us from where we
want to be is that leap of faith.
Are you ready to take that leap?

_____
_____
_____
_____
_____
_____
_____
_____
_____
_____
_____
_____

See your progress, check how you answered this question on Day 68

How are you setting the tone in your relationships?
The way you treat yourself is the way people will treat you.

_____
_____
_____
_____
_____
_____
_____
_____
_____
_____
_____
_____
_____
_____
_____

See your progress, check how you answered this question on Day 69

Day 253
___/___/___

If you are still breathing, there is room for change.

Tell yourself that when you start feeling like it's too late.

_____

_____

_____

_____

_____

_____

_____

_____

_____

_____

_____

_____

_____

_____

See your progress, check how you answered this question on Day 70

Happiness starts with you.

What are you going to do daily to make sure you are truly happy?

_____

_____

_____

_____

_____

_____

_____

_____

_____

_____

_____

_____

_____

_____

_____

_____

_____

See your progress, check how you answered this question on Day 71

Day 255

___ / ___ / ___

Each moment we have a choice.
We can continue to dwell on our past or
become the pioneer of our future.
What will you choose?

_____
_____
_____
_____
_____
_____
_____
_____
_____
_____
_____
_____

See your progress, check how you answered this question on Day 72

If you are looking for motivation to change, the fact that you are not where you want to be in life should be enough motivation.

_____

_____

_____

_____

_____

_____

_____

_____

_____

_____

_____

_____

_____

_____

_____

_____

See your progress, check how you answered this question on Day 73

Day 257

___/___/___

It's okay to have disagreement on issues.
Sometimes people have not seen things from
your perspective, so they may not understand.
It's important to remember this when you find yourself struggling with others.

See your progress, check how you answered this question on Day 74

Day 258

___ / ___ / ___

Do you really know yourself?
If you know yourself, then you will not allow someone to
say something to you that causes you to react negatively.
Remember they are outside of you, which means that they should
not have power over what takes place inside of you.

_____

_____

_____

_____

_____

_____

_____

_____

_____

_____

_____

_____

_____

_____

_____

_____

See your progress, check how you answered this question on Day 75

Day 259
___ / ___ / ___

We create these walls in our head. We tell ourselves
we can't do things because of our past experiences.
Those walls may have helped you at one point in your
life. Now, they are hindering you from moving forward.
Today's the day to start breaking down those walls.

_____
_____
_____
_____
_____
_____
_____
_____
_____
_____
_____
_____
_____

See your progress, check how you answered this question on Day 76

Day 260
__ / __ / __

Do you have goals you want to accomplish?

Do you find yourself saying, "someday"?

Where is someday located on the calendar?

Step out your comfort zone and let today be the day you make it happen.

_____

_____

_____

_____

_____

_____

_____

_____

_____

_____

_____

_____

_____

_____

_____

_____

See your progress, check how you answered this question on Day 77

Day 261
___ / ___ / ___

How are you feeling today?

What we take in and who we surround
ourselves with will shape our mindset.
Are you surrounded by love and positivity?

_____

_____

_____

_____

_____

_____

_____

_____

_____

_____

_____

_____

_____

_____

_____

_____

See your progress, check how you answered this question on Day 78

Do you know your worth?
It's important to know your value.

_____

_____

_____

_____

_____

_____

_____

_____

_____

_____

_____

_____

_____

_____

_____

_____

_____

See your progress, check how you answered this question on Day 79

Day 263

___ / ___ / ___

It's important you do not get sidetracked
by people who are not on track.
Have you checked your circle lately?

_____

_____

_____

_____

_____

_____

_____

_____

_____

_____

_____

_____

_____

_____

_____

_____

See your progress, check how you answered this question on Day 80

You will never change how people feel about
you or what they say about you.
What you can change is how you react toward them.

Day 265

___/___/___

It's hard for us to heal because we struggle with forgiveness.

Have you forgiven yourself?

Forgiving yourself is so important.

Remember you are human.

_____
_____
_____
_____
_____
_____
_____
_____
_____
_____
_____
_____
_____
_____
_____

See your progress, check how you answered this question on Day 82

How are you feeling today?

Go ahead and make a decision. You're fixated on what could go
wrong but, guess what, so many things could actually go right.

See your progress, check how you answered this question on Day 83

Day 267

___/___/___

Are you wasting time trying to impress people?
Do what you love and love what you do.

_____
_____
_____
_____
_____
_____
_____
_____
_____
_____
_____
_____
_____

See your progress, check how you answered this question on Day 84

How are you feeling today?

Everyone has the same 24 hours in a day.
What are you doing with your time?
Do you feel like you are being productive throughout the day?

_____

_____

_____

_____

_____

_____

_____

_____

_____

_____

_____

_____

_____

_____

_____

_____

See your progress, check how you answered this question on Day 85

Day 269
__ / __ / __

It is important that you are kind to yourself because
you are listening and acting on your thoughts.
What are some ways you can treat yourself better?

_____
_____
_____
_____
_____
_____
_____
_____
_____
_____
_____
_____
_____
_____
_____

See your progress, check how you answered this question on Day 86

You have something you are trying to achieve?
You may have to step out of your comfort zone to make it happen.

_____
_____
_____
_____
_____
_____
_____
_____
_____
_____
_____
_____
_____
_____
_____
_____

See your progress, check how you answered this question on Day 87

Day 271

___ / ___ / ___

If you suppress the parts of you that you do not want
to see, it can leave you feeling unbalanced.
Try looking at your entire self.

See your progress, check how you answered this question on Day 88

Do you notice negative thoughts sneaking in your mindset?
If you are aware of them, you can try and reframe them.

Day 273

__ / __ / __

Do you know what the future holds?

Why should you spend it worrying?

It is important to stay mindful on what and how you are thinking.

_____

_____

_____

_____

_____

_____

_____

_____

_____

_____

_____

_____

_____

See your progress, check how you answered this question on Day 90

Do you notice yourself having negative thoughts?
If you are aware of them, you can try to
counter them with something positive.

See your progress, check how you answered this question on Day 91

Day 275

___ / ___ / ___

Do not let your past dictate your future.
Learn from your past, forgive yourself
and others that may have hurt you.

_____

_____

_____

_____

_____

_____

_____

_____

_____

_____

_____

_____

_____

_____

_____

See your progress, check how you answered this question on Day 92

Day 276
___ / ___ / ___

How are you moving through life?
Do you find yourself rushing?
If so, why? What are you trying to achieve?

_____

_____

_____

_____

_____

_____

_____

_____

_____

_____

_____

_____

_____

_____

See your progress, check how you answered this question on Day 93

Day 277

___ / ___ / ___

We are conditioned to be doing what everyone else is doing.

Try living an intentional life.

Do you feel you have been intentional about doing what's best for you?

If not, how can you be more intentional?

_____
_____
_____
_____
_____
_____
_____
_____
_____
_____
_____
_____
_____
_____

See your progress, check how you answered this question on Day 94

Day 278
__ / __ / __

Do you feel like the people in your life are adding value?
Take some time to evaluate how the
people in your life are treating you.
Are the relationships reciprocal?

See your progress, check how you answered this question on Day 95

Day 279
___ / ___ / ___

What did you do yesterday that led you
towards the direction of your goal?
If the answer is nothing, plan on doing something this week.

_____

_____

_____

_____

_____

_____

_____

_____

_____

_____

_____

_____

_____

See your progress, check how you answered this question on Day 96

If you find yourself struggling with other
people's perspectives, understand that everyone
is different and has different stories to tell.
Sometimes you just have to agree to disagree.

_____
_____
_____
_____
_____
_____
_____
_____
_____
_____
_____
_____
_____
_____
_____
_____

See your progress, check how you answered this question on Day 97

Day 281
___ / ___ / ___

One of the greatest things you can do for
yourself is learn who you really are.
When you learn who you are, no one can take that away.
Who are you?

_____

_____

_____

_____

_____

_____

_____

_____

_____

_____

_____

_____

_____

See your progress, check how you answered this question on Day 98

Sometimes we build walls in our head that
prohibit us from growing in life.
It is important to think about the barriers to our growth.
What mental walls have you built?
It is important that we recognize and stay mindful of the things that hold us back.

_____
_____
_____
_____
_____
_____
_____
_____
_____
_____
_____
_____
_____
_____
_____
_____

See your progress, check how you answered this question on Day 99

Day 283

___/___/___

Forgiving yourself is important.

You are human.

If you are holding on to something you have done,

learn how to forgive yourself. It's necessary for growth.

See your progress, check how you answered this question on Day 100

We have goals, we make plans, but we fail to execute.

Use what you can and just do it.

Its time to start making your goals a reality.

_____

_____

_____

_____

_____

_____

_____

_____

_____

_____

_____

_____

_____

_____

_____

See your progress, check how you answered this question on Day 101

Day 285

___/___/___

Life is too short not to be happy. Happiness starts on the inside.

How are you feeling today?

_____

_____

_____

_____

_____

_____

_____

_____

_____

_____

_____

_____

_____

_____

See your progress, check how you answered this question on Day 102

We miss out on life when we are worrying about the future.

Are you living in the moment?

_____

_____

_____

_____

_____

_____

_____

_____

_____

_____

_____

_____

_____

_____

_____

See your progress, check how you answered this question on Day 103

Day 287

__ / __ / __

Sometimes you may not feel like doing what
you have to do to reach your goal.
It is important to push pass that feeling and think of
the results that you will gain when you achieve your goal.
You can do this.
You just have to have the faith to believe in yourself.

See your progress, check how you answered this question on Day 104

If you are a parent, make sure you are really
listening to your children. The behaviors you are
observing could actually be a cry for help.

_____

_____

_____

_____

_____

_____

_____

_____

_____

_____

_____

_____

_____

_____

_____

_____

See your progress, check how you answered this question on Day 105

Day 289

__ / __ / __

Did you know that faith drives out fear?
In order to have faith, it's important you are
feeding your faith. If you are not being intentional
on feeding your faith, then fear will always win.

_____

_____

_____

_____

_____

_____

_____

_____

_____

_____

_____

_____

_____

_____

See your progress, check how you answered this question on Day 106

Do you have something you are trying to accomplish but find yourself stuck? You have to make a commitment and be consistent.

Day 291

__ / __ / __

Think about how a tree started.

It was once a seed.

Everything doesn't start big.

How are you feeling today?

See your progress, check how you answered this question on Day 108

How are you feeling today?

Start focusing on you and take it one day at a time

_____
_____
_____
_____
_____
_____
_____
_____
_____
_____
_____
_____
_____
_____
_____
_____
_____
_____

See your progress, check how you answered this question on Day 109

Day 293

___ / ___ / ___

Letting go is so hard but, waiting can be even
harder. Ask yourself, "What do I deserve?"
You deserve the best! You have to have the faith to believe that.

See your progress, check how you answered this question on Day 110

Look at what you have now to achieve your goal.
Just because it's not everything you want, doesn't
mean you can't use what you have in front of you.
It starts with a paper and pen. Start writing your vision down.

_____

_____

_____

_____

_____

_____

_____

_____

_____

_____

_____

_____

_____

_____

_____

See your progress, check how you answered this question on Day 111

Day 295

___ / ___ / ___

Do not allow the people who hate on you discourage you.

You can think of them as your motivator.

You can't change a hater.

_____
_____
_____
_____
_____
_____
_____
_____
_____
_____
_____
_____
_____
_____

See your progress, check how you answered this question on Day 112

Day 296

__ / __ / __

We all have choices. We can be ourselves or we
can be who we think others want us to be.
Every morning, choose to be you.
It feels so good to just wake up and be you.
Do you feel like you are being true to yourself?

_____

_____

_____

_____

_____

_____

_____

_____

_____

_____

_____

_____

_____

_____

_____

_____

See your progress, check how you answered this question on Day 113

Day 297

___/___/___

Just because something did not work
out it does not mean it's over.
Look at the things you call failures as life lessons.
Change your perspective.

See your progress, check how you answered this question on Day 114

It's time you stop worrying about how others feel about you.
You can't stop someone from judging you.
If you want to stop caring about being judged, you have to
learn yourself and become authentic. When you are living YOUR life,
and being authentic, no one can ever take that away from you..

Day 299
___ / ___ / ___

It is important to tell yourself each day, "One day at a time."
Life is a journey, not a race.

_____

_____

_____

_____

_____

_____

_____

_____

_____

_____

_____

_____

_____

See your progress, check how you answered this question on Day 116

Self-care is a major part of success.

Learn how to set boundaries and be consistent.

_____

_____

_____

_____

_____

_____

_____

_____

_____

_____

_____

_____

_____

_____

_____

_____

See your progress, check how you answered this question on Day 117

Day 301

___ / ___ / ___

It is important that you stop comparing
yourself to other people and look in the mirror to
compare yourself to who you were yesterday.
Always strive for a better you.

_____
_____
_____
_____
_____
_____
_____
_____
_____
_____
_____
_____

See your progress, check how you answered this question on Day 118

If you can be intentional on distancing yourself from the
negativity, you will find yourself in a different space mentally.

See your progress, check how you answered this question on Day 119

Day 303
___ / ___ / ___

Stop looking at yourself in a negative way because
you are different. Being different is okay.

See your progress, check how you answered this question on Day 120

Day 304
__ / __ / __

There is room in life for everyone to win.

Everything is not a competition.

Your only competition should be a better version of you.

See your progress, check how you answered this question on Day 121

Day 305

__ / __ / __

Stop letting fear control you.
Try turning fear into hope.

_____

_____

_____

_____

_____

_____

_____

_____

_____

_____

_____

_____

_____

_____

See your progress, check how you answered this question on Day 122

How are you feeling today?

If what you are doing isn't working, why
not try something different?
Anything you need to try differently?

_____

_____

_____

_____

_____

_____

_____

_____

_____

_____

_____

_____

_____

_____

_____

_____

See your progress, check how you answered this question on Day 123

Day 307

__/__/__

Stop saying, "one day I will do it" and just make it happen today.
You can make it happen by writing a realistic plan for yourself.

_____
_____
_____
_____
_____
_____
_____
_____
_____
_____
_____
_____
_____
_____

See your progress, check how you answered this question on Day 124

Day 308

___ / ___ / ___

Do you know who you are?

We are conditioned to be who society says we should be.

If you feel you do not know who you are,

you can try letting go of societal norms.

See your progress, check how you answered this question on Day 125

Day 309

___/___/___

It is important that we learn the difference
between our wants and our needs.
Sometimes the things that we hold on to
(wants) keep us from receiving what we need.

_____
_____
_____
_____
_____
_____
_____
_____
_____
_____
_____
_____

See your progress, check how you answered this question on Day 126

Day 310
__ / __ / __

Sometimes you may wonder if you are winning in life.
If you ask yourself this question, often it's because you continue
to focus on the things you lack and forget to embrace what you have.

_____

_____

_____

_____

_____

_____

_____

_____

_____

_____

_____

_____

_____

_____

_____

_____

See your progress, check how you answered this question on Day 127

Day 311
__ / __ / __

We all have choices.

It is time you start taking responsibility for your actions.

Do you feel like you are taking responsibility for your actions?

_____
_____
_____
_____
_____
_____
_____
_____
_____
_____
_____
_____
_____

See your progress, check how you answered this question on Day 128

Setting boundaries is an important life skill.
Do you feel like you are setting boundaries to take care of yourself?
If not, how can you start setting boundaries today?

See your progress, check how you answered this question on Day 129

Day 313
__ / __ / __

Imagine how intentional your life can be if
you start thinking before you act.

See your progress, check how you answered this question on Day 130

Do you find yourself stressing over things that are not in your control? If you do not have control over it, learn how to let it go.

_____
_____
_____
_____
_____
_____
_____
_____
_____
_____
_____
_____
_____
_____
_____
_____

See your progress, check how you answered this question on Day 131

Day 315

__ / __ / __

Stop dreaming about what you want to do.

Just go out and do it.

Are you doing what you need to do to make your dreams come true?

See your progress, check how you answered this question on Day 132

It is important that you stop looking for validation.
If you have no one rooting you on, learn
how to be your biggest motivator.

_____

Day 317

__ / __ / __

Know yourself and embrace your uniqueness.

How are you feeling today?

See your progress, check how you answered this question on Day 134

Is your life being controlled by internal wounds from your past?
It is important that you analyze yourself and your decisions.

_____
_____
_____
_____
_____
_____
_____
_____
_____
_____
_____
_____
_____
_____

See your progress, check how you answered this question on Day 135

Day 319
___ / ___ / ___

Sometimes we are worrying so much that we
forget to start working on our goals.
Get out of your head and start making your goals happen.

_____

_____

_____

_____

_____

_____

_____

_____

_____

_____

_____

_____

See your progress, check how you answered this question on Day 136

Day 320
__/__/__

Your relationships should be reciprocal.
Make sure you are not the only one giving.

See your progress, check how you answered this question on Day 137

Day 321

___ / ___ / ___

Consistency and commitment are a major key to success.

_____

_____

_____

_____

_____

_____

_____

_____

_____

_____

_____

_____

_____

See your progress, check how you answered this question on Day 138

Have you experienced trauma?

If you are dealing with the trauma, you are constantly triggered.

Dealing with trauma allows you to maintain control over your mind.

_____

_____

_____

_____

_____

_____

_____

_____

_____

_____

_____

_____

_____

_____

_____

_____

See your progress, check how you answered this question on Day 139

Day 323
__ / __ / __

Life doesn't always happen like we expect it to happen.
I challenge you to let go of expectations.
If you do that, you can live in the moment.

_____

_____

_____

_____

_____

_____

_____

_____

_____

_____

_____

_____

_____

See your progress, check how you answered this question on Day 140

Day 324
__ / __ / __

If you have goals that you are trying to accomplish,
being consistent is a major key.

_____
_____
_____
_____
_____
_____
_____
_____
_____
_____
_____
_____
_____
_____
_____
_____

See your progress, check how you answered this question on Day 141

Day 325

___ / ___ / ___

Did you know that you matter?

Sometimes you may feel drained.

Sometimes it's due to the fact that you are not putting yourself first.

Are you taking care of yourself everyday?

_____

_____

_____

_____

_____

_____

_____

_____

_____

_____

_____

_____

_____

_____

See your progress, check how you answered this question on Day 142

Day 326

__ / __ / __

Because we can pride ourselves as being strong, we fail to
realize how our broken pieces in life have hindered us.
We continue to grow physically, but mentally we are stuck.
Do you find yourself stuck?

See your progress, check how you answered this question on Day 143

Day 327

__ / __ / __

Forgiveness does not excuse what happened to you.
Forgiveness will allow you to move forward in life.

_____
_____
_____
_____
_____
_____
_____
_____
_____
_____
_____
_____
_____
_____

See your progress, check how you answered this question on Day 144

Do you love yourself?
Forgive yourself for past mistakes.
This is an important part of growth.

Day 329

___ / ___ / ___

Feeling stuck in life?

If yes, have you accepted where you are in life.

Acceptance is acknowledging your current reality.

If it's not where you want to be, you can plan to make changes in your life.

You have to be intentional for the plan to work

_____

_____

_____

_____

_____

_____

_____

_____

_____

_____

_____

_____

_____

_____

See your progress, check how you answered this question on Day 146

Day 330
___ / ___ / ___

How do you define being whole?
Being whole does not mean you are perfect.
It simply means accepting who you are and
learning to be content with it. If it's not who you want to be,
you can work on achieving certain goals for yourself.

_____

_____

_____

_____

_____

_____

_____

_____

_____

_____

_____

_____

_____

_____

_____

_____

See your progress, check how you answered this question on Day 147

Day 331

___/___/___

Keep pushing forward.

Having hope is so necessary in life.

_____

_____

_____

_____

_____

_____

_____

_____

_____

_____

_____

_____

_____

_____

See your progress, check how you answered this question on Day 148

If what you are doing is not working, it is
important to try something different.

Day 333

__ / __ / __

Even through your darkest days, you must fight hard
to remind yourself after the rain there is a rainbow.

See your progress, check how you answered this question on Day 150

Authenticity is key.

Be yourself so no one can ever take that away from you.

_____

_____

_____

_____

_____

_____

_____

_____

_____

_____

_____

_____

_____

_____

_____

_____

_____

See your progress, check how you answered this question on Day 151

Day 335

___ / ___ / ___

What and whom are you inviting in your life?

Make sure you are constantly assessing the way you treat yourself.

You deserve the best.

_____

_____

_____

_____

_____

_____

_____

_____

_____

_____

_____

_____

_____

_____

_____

See your progress, check how you answered this question on Day 152

You have a purpose in life.

Day 337

___ / ___ / ___

Imagine what could happen if we started to highlight our joys?
In this very moment, right now it's important
to focus on inner peace and happiness.

_____

_____

_____

_____

_____

_____

_____

_____

_____

_____

_____

_____

See your progress, check how you answered this question on Day 154

You may not be here tomorrow.

Why waste your energy living in fear?

_____
_____
_____
_____
_____
_____
_____
_____
_____
_____
_____
_____
_____
_____
_____
_____

See your progress, check how you answered this question on Day 155

Day 339

___ / ___ / ___

What is more important to you?

Your material possessions or your inner peace and happiness?

_____
_____
_____
_____
_____
_____
_____
_____
_____
_____
_____
_____
_____
_____

See your progress, check how you answered this question on Day 156

Day 340
__ / __ / __

You may be your own hinderance to growing to your full potential.
Can you think of areas where you are
hindering yourself from growing?

See your progress, check how you answered this question on Day 157

Day 341

___ / ___ / ___

Just because you are right, doesn't mean
the other person is wrong.
It is important you understand that there are
people who may have different life experiences.
Take that into account when a disagreement takes place.

See your progress, check how you answered this question on Day 158

Day 342

___ / ___ / ___

Did you know that you will repeat the things you do not repair?

What areas in your life need repairs?

_____

_____

_____

_____

_____

_____

_____

_____

_____

_____

_____

_____

_____

_____

_____

_____

_____

See your progress, check how you answered this question on Day 159

Day 343

___ / ___ / ___

Are you using band aids to deal with your problems in life?

It's important to not cover up our problems with temporary fixes.

What band aids are you using in life.

_____

_____

_____

_____

_____

_____

_____

_____

_____

_____

_____

_____

_____

See your progress, check how you answered this question on Day 160

We miss out on life when we worry about the future.

Try living in the moment.

_____

_____

_____

_____

_____

_____

_____

_____

_____

_____

_____

_____

_____

_____

_____

_____

See your progress, check how you answered this question on Day 161

Day 345
__/__/__

What if I told you that your past does not have to keep you stuck?

You can keep going.

You are destined for greatness.

You just must have the faith to believe that.

_____

_____

_____

_____

_____

_____

_____

_____

_____

_____

_____

_____

_____

_____

_____

_____

See your progress, check how you answered this question on Day 162

Day 346

___ / ___ / ___

Life is too short for dreams.
Get up, get out and make memories.

See your progress, check how you answered this question on Day 163

Day 347

___ / ___ / ___

If you are trying to create a positive life style,
do not be afraid of losing people.
Be afraid of losing yourself.

_____
_____
_____
_____
_____
_____
_____
_____
_____
_____
_____
_____
_____
_____
_____

See your progress, check how you answered this question on Day 164

Day 348

___ / ___ / ___

Having low self-esteem can hinder you from moving forward.
How do you really feel about yourself?
If you feel like your esteem is low, continue
challenging yourself to speak positive over your life.

_____

_____

_____

_____

_____

_____

_____

_____

_____

_____

_____

_____

_____

_____

_____

_____

See your progress, check how you answered this question on Day 165

Day 349
___ / ___ / ___

How do you start your day?

Do you look on social media first thing in the morning?

Try starting it with meditation.

Create time to start your day off right.

_____

_____

_____

_____

_____

_____

_____

_____

_____

_____

_____

_____

_____

See your progress, check how you answered this question on Day 166

If you are in a relationship; Is knowing yourself important?
If not, then its important you make it a
priority to get to know yourself.

See your progress, check how you answered this question on Day 167

Day 351

___ / ___ / ___

Forgiveness is hard but necessary.

If we can't forgive, we create a wall around our heart

that will block us from receiving and spreading love.

_____

_____

_____

_____

_____

_____

_____

_____

_____

_____

_____

_____

_____

_____

See your progress, check how you answered this question on Day 168

If you find yourself in a negative cycle in life, you
must first learn how to be conscious and present.
Once you are present and see the affects it has
on you, you can plan to make concrete changes.

Day 353

__ / __ / __

In life, we tend to suffer because we are more
concerned about what we look like on the outside
and not concerned about what's going on internally.

How are you feeling today?

See your progress, check how you answered this question on Day 170

How are you feeling today?

Make sure you are constantly doing self-assessments
and taking responsibility for your actions.

_____

_____

_____

_____

_____

_____

_____

_____

_____

_____

_____

_____

_____

_____

_____

See your progress, check how you answered this question on Day 171

Day 355

___/___/___

Try living in the now.

If you do that, you can focus on the today.

_____

_____

_____

_____

_____

_____

_____

_____

_____

_____

_____

_____

_____

_____

See your progress, check how you answered this question on Day 172

Day 356

___ / ___ / ___

If not now, then when?
Time waits for nobody.
What are you putting off doing?
Make plans today.

See your progress, check how you answered this question on Day 173

Day 357

___/___/___

Are you in a relationship and feeling unhappy?

If you are not happy with who you are outside of a relationship,

how do you expect to find happiness in someone else?

_____

_____

_____

_____

_____

_____

_____

_____

_____

_____

_____

_____

_____

_____

See your progress, check how you answered this question on Day 174

Day 358

___ / ___ / ___

How much time are you really investing in yourself?
We invest in the things we care about.
Make sure your needs are being met.

_____
_____
_____
_____
_____
_____
_____
_____
_____
_____
_____
_____
_____
_____
_____

See your progress, check how you answered this question on Day 175

Day 359
__ / __ / __

As children, we had no control over our environment.

As an adult, we can create the environment

in which we want to see ourselves.

This means letting go of negative energy and negative people.

_____

_____

_____

_____

_____

_____

_____

_____

_____

_____

_____

_____

_____

See your progress, check how you answered this question on Day 176

Day 360

___ / ___ / ___

Are you feeling stuck and need motivation?

Life is short.

Let that marinate because time waits for no one.

_____
_____
_____
_____
_____
_____
_____
_____
_____
_____
_____
_____
_____
_____
_____

See your progress, check how you answered this question on Day 177

Day 361
__ / __ / __

Are you making every moment count?
If the answer is no, start being intentional
about living in the present.

_____
_____
_____
_____
_____
_____
_____
_____
_____
_____
_____
_____
_____
_____

See your progress, check how you answered this question on Day 178

You owe yourself the same love you give to other people.
You deserve the best and you are worthy.

_____

_____

_____

_____

_____

_____

_____

_____

_____

_____

_____

_____

_____

_____

_____

See your progress, check how you answered this question on Day 179

Day 363

___ / ___ / ___

If we start agreeing to disagree, it can honor our differences while offering a solution.

_____
_____
_____
_____
_____
_____
_____
_____
_____
_____
_____
_____
_____
_____

See your progress, check how you answered this question on Day 180

Day 364

___ / ___ / ___

Do you find yourself worrying all the time?
If yes, ask yourself, "Do I have control over it?"
If the answer is no, learn how to let it go.

Day 365
__ / __ / __

How are you feeling today?

How do you move forward if you continue to look back?

_____

_____

_____

_____

_____

_____

_____

_____

_____

_____

_____

_____

_____

See your progress, check how you answered this question on Day 182

What is on your to do list today?

Living in the moment should always be on your to do list.

See your progress, check how you answered this question on Day 183